Arabian Nights

A graphic classic by
Terry West

Based on traditional stories

SCHOLASTIC INC.
New York Toronto London Auckland Sydney
Mexico City New Delhi Hong Kong

Penciller
Michael Lilly

Layouts
Michael Lilly

Colors, Inks, and Letters
Digital Chameleon

Cover Art
Michael Lilly

Project Management
Michael Apice

ISBN 0-439-31267-1

7 8 9 10   40   11 10

Arabian Nights

Scheherazade (SHEH-HEH-RA-ZOD) HAS MARRIED THE SULTAN (KING). BUT THE SULTAN TRUSTS NO ONE. HE HAS SWORN TO KILL SCHEHERAZADE. SHE MUST FIND A WAY TO HELP HIM — AND SAVE HERSELF.

SCHEHERAZADE LEARNS THAT THE SULTAN IS HAVING NIGHTMARES. SO, EVERY NIGHT, FOR 1,001 NIGHTS, SHE TELLS HIM A STORY. THE STORIES HELP THE SULTAN SLEEP. WITH EACH STORY SHE LIVES ANOTHER DAY.

THE STORIES THAT SCHEHERAZADE TELLS ARE FOLK TALES THAT ARE CENTURIES OLD. THESE FOLK TALES COME FROM THE MIDDLE EAST, EGYPT, AND INDIA. THEY ARE STILL ENJOYED TODAY. IN FACT, YOU PROBABLY KNOW AT LEAST ONE OF THEM--THE STORY OF "ALADDIN."

BUT THE SULTAN HAD AN EVIL BROTHER WHO WANTED THE KINGDOM FOR HIMSELF. HE WAS ABLE TO CONVINCE THE SULTAN'S WIFE TO HELP HIM. TOGETHER, THEY MADE A PLAN TO KILL THE SULTAN.

My brother doesn't do enough for you. When I am sultan, I will shower you with riches!

THE SULTAN LEARNED OF THE PLAN. WHEN HIS WIFE AND BROTHER TRIED TO KILL HIM, HE WAS READY FOR THEM.

Betrayed by the two people I love most in the world!

THE SULTAN THREW A SPEAR AT HIS BROTHER. BUT HE MISSED. HE HIT HIS WIFE INSTEAD. SHE WAS KILLED INSTANTLY.

NO!!

EVER SINCE THAT AWFUL NIGHT, THE SULTAN HAD TROUBLE SLEEPING. EVERY NIGHT HE SUFFERED THE SAME NIGHTMARE.

NO!! NO!!

IN THE NIGHTMARE, HE REMEMBERED HOW HIS WIFE AND BROTHER BETRAYED HIM. AND HE REMEMBERED HOW HE HAD STOPPED THEM.

THE SULTAN'S FATHER WAS WORRIED.

My son, you must take a new wife. It is the law of our land. If you do not marry soon, the kingdom will go to your brother.

I will never let my brother sit upon this throne. But, I do not want another wife.

THE SULTAN CAME UP WITH A SHOCKING SOLUTION. IT WAS MADNESS.

I am ready to choose a bride. But I will have her killed on our wedding night. No wife will get the chance to betray me again!! You are my advisor, what do you think?

Your majesty, I must speak truthfully. Please forgive me, but I don't think this is a very good idea.

THE SULTAN HAD GONE MAD. THE SULTAN'S ADVISOR DIDN'T KNOW WHAT TO DO. BUT HIS DAUGHTER, SCHEHERAZADE, HAD A PLAN OF HER OWN.

Father, I will marry the sultan.

My daughter, I cannot allow you to do this. It would mean certain death!

Father, I must do this. Please, trust me.

The sultan and I grew up together in this very palace.

WE USED TO PLAY IN THE PALACE GARDEN. HE WAS A SWEET AND KIND BOY.

I'm going to put an end to this madness! I don't know how, exactly. But, I'll find a way.

SCHEHERAZADE WAS BRAVE. BUT WAS SHE WISE? HOW COULD SHE STOP THE SULTAN'S TERRIBLE PLAN?

WITHIN DAYS THE SULTAN AND SCHEHERAZADE WERE WED. SCHEHERAZADE WAS DOOMED... OR WAS SHE?

THE PEOPLE WERE HAPPY TO SEE THE SULTAN WED. THEY HOPED IT MEANT THAT THINGS WERE BACK TO NORMAL.

THE SULTAN WAS DETERMINED TO CARRY OUT HIS PLAN.

Tonight you must die, my bride. I can trust no one. If only these nightmares would stop...

SUDDENLY, SCHEHERAZADE HAD AN IDEA.

Nightmares, your majesty?

I have the same nightmare every night. It's driving me mad!

THE SULTAN WAS INTERESTED IN SCHEHERAZADE'S PLAN.

SCHEHERAZADE HAS DECIDED TO TELL THE SULTAN A BEDTIME STORY.

ONE DAY WHILE GATHERING WOOD, ALI BABA SAW SOMETHING STRANGE. FORTY THIEVES WERE ENTERING A SECRET CAVE. WITH SOME WORDS, THEY MADE THE CAVE OPEN.

AFTER THE THIEVES LEFT, ALI BABA REPEATED THE WORDS AND ENTERED THE CAVE.

HE FILLED HIS POCKETS WITH GOLD AND QUICKLY LEFT THE CAVE.

ALI BABA OFFERED TO SHARE HIS GOLD WITH HIS BROTHER. BUT KASIM WANTED MORE.

Share this gold with me, my brother.

You must tell me where this cave is!

Open sesame.

KASIM WAS GREEDY. HE SPENT A LONG TIME IN THE CAVE GATHERING TREASURE.

WHEN KASIM WAS FINALLY READY TO LEAVE, HE FORGOT THE PASSWORD. HE WAS TRAPPED INSIDE THE CAVE. THE FORTY THIEVES RETURNED AND KILLED HIM.

We'll teach you to steal our stolen treasure!

WHEN KASIM DIDN'T RETURN, ALI BABA RETURNED TO THE CAVE TO LOOK FOR HIM. THE THIEVES HAD LEFT KASIM'S BODY AS A WARNING TO OTHERS.

Oh, my brother! What have they done to you?

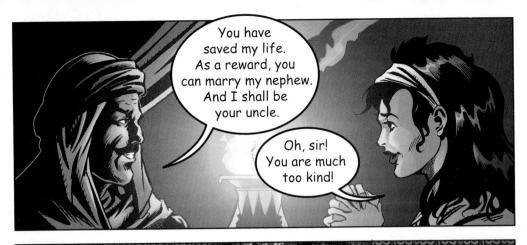

THE SULTAN SLEPT SOUNDLY AFTER LISTENING TO THE STORY OF ALI BABA.

I thought a good bedtime story might do the trick.

Have I told you the story of Sinbad the Sailor, yet, my sweet?

And tomorrow night I'll tell you about Sinbad's seventh voyage.

No, let's hear about this Sinbad character. Scheherazade, you really do tell the best stories.

EACH NIGHT SCHEHERAZADE TOLD ANOTHER STORY. EACH STORY KEPT SCHEHERAZADE ALIVE FOR ANOTHER DAY.

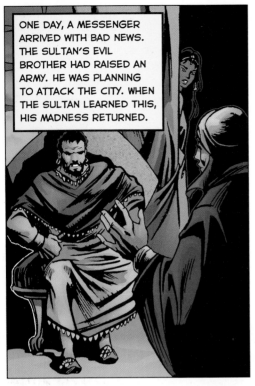

ONE DAY, A MESSENGER ARRIVED WITH BAD NEWS. THE SULTAN'S EVIL BROTHER HAD RAISED AN ARMY. HE WAS PLANNING TO ATTACK THE CITY. WHEN THE SULTAN LEARNED THIS, HIS MADNESS RETURNED.

I have allowed myself to get soft. No one can be trusted, especially my wife, Scheherazade. Tonight she dies!

SCHEHERAZADE NOW WOULD HAVE TO TELL THE GREATEST STORY OF ALL... OR LOSE HER LIFE!

Your majesty, have I told you the tale of Aladdin?

ALADDIN WAS A YOUNG MAN. HE SPENT MOST OF HIS DAYS PLAYING WITH HIS FRIENDS. AFTER HIS FATHER DIED, HIS MOTHER WORKED HARD TO KEEP THEM FED.

I'm afraid my son, Aladdin, will never grow up.

ONE DAY, A RICH MAN CAME ALONG. HE SAID HE WAS ALADDIN'S LONG LOST UNCLE.

Hello, my young nephew.

THIS UNCLE SEEMED VERY KIND. HE BROUGHT FOOD TO ALADDIN AND HIS MOTHER. HE BOUGHT ALADDIN NEW CLOTHES.

Please accept this small gift.

ALADDIN'S UNCLE ASKED ALADDIN IF HE'D LIKE TO TAKE A WALK. IT WAS A LONG WALK. THEY WALKED FOR HOURS.

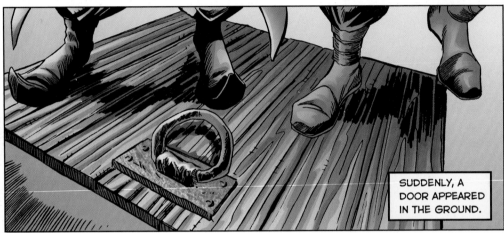

SUDDENLY, A DOOR APPEARED IN THE GROUND.

ALADDIN DIDN'T KNOW IT, BUT THIS MAN WASN'T HIS UNCLE. HE WAS AN EVIL MAGICIAN.

Beneath this door is a treasure, which will be yours. All you must do is go below and get me the lamp. Here is my ring for good luck.

SUDDENLY, ALADDIN FELT AFRAID.

Give it to me now, you stupid boy!

THE LAMP WOULD HAVE MADE THE MAGICIAN VERY POWERFUL. BUT HE HAD TO RECEIVE THE LAMP FROM ANOTHER'S HAND. IF HE GRABBED IT FOR HIMSELF, IT WOULDN'T WORK.

If you won't give it to me, then rot with it down there!

ALADDIN WAS TRAPPED IN THE DARK. IT WAS COLD, SO HE RUBBED HIS HANDS.

I am the genie of the ring. What is your wish?

Can you get me out of here?

THE RING ON ALADDIN'S FINGER HAS SPECIAL POWERS. IT HAD BELONGED TO THE MAGICIAN.

THE GENIE FREED ALADDIN FROM THAT UNDERGROUND CAVE. THEN ALADDIN WALKED HOME. HE TOLD HIS MOTHER WHAT HAPPENED.

AS ALADDIN'S MOTHER RUBBED THE LAMP, SMOKE BEGAN TO POUR OUT OF IT. SUDDENLY, A GENIE APPEARED. IT WAS EVEN BIGGER THAN THE OTHER ONE.

....And then he kicked the door shut and trapped me under the ground!

Aladdin, what will we do without your uncle? He was such a great help to us. Maybe we can sell this old lamp for some food. I'll shine it up.

I am the genie of the lamp. What is your wish?

Food!

Fine clothes! Riches!

ALADDIN CAME BACK TO FIND HIS CASTLE AND HIS PRINCESS GONE. SOMEONE TOLD ALADDIN ABOUT THE OLD MAN WITH THE WAGON FULL OF LAMPS.

The old magician came back!

THEN ALADDIN REMEMBERED THE GENIE OF THE RING...

Genie of the ring, take me to where the princess is!

THE GENIE OF THE RING TOOK ALADDIN TO A STRANGE LAND.

ALADDIN AND THE PRINCESS QUICKLY MADE A PLAN.

You must hide, my darling. The magician will soon return. Don't worry. I know what to do.

Please be careful, my darling. The magician is a dangerous man.

THE PRINCESS PUT POISON IN THE MAGICIAN'S CUP.

Forget about Aladdin. Be my wife!

Okay. But first, drink up!

ALADDIN AND THE PRINCESS DIDN'T HAVE TO WORRY ABOUT THE MAGICIAN ANYMORE. ALADDIN QUICKLY FOUND HIS LAMP. HE ASKED THE GENIE OF THE LAMP TO TAKE THEM AND THE CASTLE BACK HOME.

THEY RETURNED HOME AND THEY LIVED HAPPILY EVER AFTER.